DOCTOR WHO
QUIZ BOOK OF SPACE
MICHAEL HOLT

Again, the Doctor and his companions take off in the TARDIS to rove through time and space and solve some of the great mysteries of the Universe. Join in the great adventure of discovery with puzzles and experiments to do yourself. Have fun and amaze your friends!

Doctor Who Quiz Book of SPACE

Michael Holt

Illustrated by Rowan Barnes-Murphy

A Magnet Book

Also in Magnet Books:
Doctor Who Quiz Book of Dinosaurs
Doctor Who Quiz Book of Magic
Doctor Who Quiz Book of Science

First published in 1983 as a Magnet paperback
by Methuen Children's Books Ltd
11 New Fetter Lane, London EC4P 4EE
Text copyright © 1983 Michael Holt
Illustrations copyright © 1983 Rowan Barnes-Murphy
Cover artwork copyright © 1983 Methuen Children's Books Ltd
BBC copyright photograph
Published by arrangement with the
British Broadcasting Corporation
Printed in Great Britain
by Cox & Wyman Ltd, Reading
ISBN 0 416 20450 3

Contents

Those Daring Young Men in their Flying Machines

The Doctor and his two young companions Tegan and Turlough had been discussing their next trip in the TARDIS – and had chosen Space.

'Before we explore outer space,' said the Doctor, 'I think we ought to see the conquest of inner space!' The Doctor sported his natty red-piped beige frock-coat over a cricketing sweater and striped ducks.

'Inner space, Doctor?' said Tegan. 'I'm filling it now!' She was pacing about the TARDIS' Control Room in a belted white shirt, white shorts and scuffed tennis shoes, munching a soya Space Snack. She was slim enough not to have to worry about her waistline.

'The air about us, Tegan,' the Doctor explained. 'The conquest of the Earth's atmosphere, I mean. Let's witness the birth of the aeroplane and its parents – the inventors Orville and Wilbur Wright.'

'When and where?' asked Turlough who was lolling in a swivel chair, spruce in black trousers, wing collar, red and black striped tie. Red-haired and blue-blooded, he looked the very picture of an English public schoolboy, a strong contrast to Tegan's brash Australian outback girl.

'I've already programmed the Time Console for Kitty Hawk, North Carolina in America – the time: ten o'clock, December the seventeeth, 1903. Let's go and see history being made!' And with that the Doctor hit the Time Warp key.

The TARDIS came to rest, with its familiar clanking noise like the call of whales under the sea, on a beach at Kitty Hawk. As the trio stepped out of the TARDIS, they were met by the boom of the Atlantic rollers as they crashed on the long, sandy beach, whipped up by a steady, southerly gale – Force 8, or about sixty kilometres an hour. Over the dunes

7

the Doctor spotted two young men struggling to pull a small biplane out of a makeshift hangar. One of them caught sight of the trio and waved them over. 'Don't suppose you could lend a hand?' he bellowed through the wind to them as they drew near.

The Doctor recognised him from old snaps as thirty-six-year-old Wilbur Wright. Orville, thirty-two years old, sported a large moustache and both were wearing dark blazers and peaked caps.

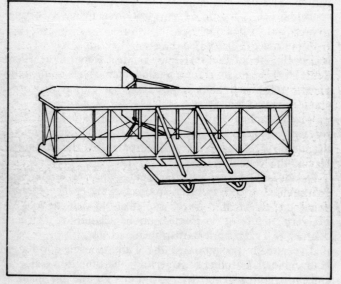

With Tegan and Turlough's help, the Wright brothers slid their little biplane on its wooden skids over to two long wooden rails, no longer than the thirteen-metre wingspan of the *Flyer*, as they called their plane. The rails were set in the sand facing *into* the wind to help 'up' the speed of the plane. They lifted the 'crate', held together as it seemed by wire, onto a small trolley that ran along the rails.

'This is our *Flyer*!' Wilbur shouted to the Doctor as he put his hand in his pocket and tossed a nickel. He nodded to his brother, Orville, who climbed gingerly onto the lower wing of the plane. He lay down beside the tiny motor-mower of an engine, only twelve horse power, linked by two bicycle chains to two large wooden propellors at the back, behind the top wing. They were fixed there so as to push the plane forward. Jutting out in front, like a ship's bowsprit, was a pair of small wings, to steady the Flyer's flight. Way out behind, on open struts, stuck two crude rudders.

Orville checked the steering: he pulled on two cords beside him to swivel the rudders.

Wilbur asked Tegan and Turlough to each hold a wing tip to steady the *Flyer* for take-off. He then ran round to the front and began cranking the engine. With a bang and a splutter the two-stroke engine coughed into life. At first Wilbur, Tegan and Turlough held onto the plane until Orville nodded to them to let go. As one they released the shuddering plane – and it slid forward along the wooden rails, gathering speed. At the end of the rails Orville pulled on the cords to twist the wings. The *Flyer* gave an answering lift and up she rose to a dizzying three metres off the ground, leaving the trolley behind.

Orville looked down and saw he was a little too high off the ground for safety. By yanking sharply at the cords he safely skimmed several sand dunes, until he pulled *too* sharply. The *Flyer*'s nose dipped. He tried to correct his mistake. Too late! The *Flyer*'s skids touched the ground. Touch down! The flight was over. The plane skidded to a stop in the sand.

Orville cut the engine and, as the propellors slowed to a stop, he clambered out. Wilbur ran up to him, clutching his stop-watch.

'Twelve seconds, Orv! The best flight time yet! C'mon, let's pace it out.' Together they strode back to the end of the rails.

'Thirty-nine yards!'

The Doctor did a lightning calculation and shouted back, 'Thirty-six *metres*, Mr Wright! Oh, by the way, these are my companions, Tegan and Turlough, and I'm the Doctor.'

'My pleasure!' Wilbur beamed at the trio. 'This here is my

young brother Orville. We're the Wrights, inventors and —'

'Pilots!' Orville bubbled. 'Say, would you good folks lend us a hand . . . once more? We want to make another test flight.'

Tegan and Turlough willingly helped the Wright Brothers lug the *Flyer* back to the wooden rails. There they lifted it onto the wooden trolley and slid it back to the start of the run. Orville climbed in again, and Wilbur held onto the *Flyer*'s right wing to steady its take-off.

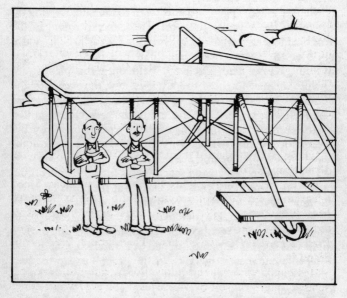

The Doctor took a snap of the exciting historical occasion with the brother's box camera, a Kodak 'Brownie'. This is the famous photo to be seen in the books, of the Wright's famous flight at Kitty Hawk. The Doctor and his companions are nowhere to be seen in the picture, for the Doctor had told Tegan and Turlough to keep 'well out of the shot' for fear of upsetting history!

Orville made a perfect take-off and the *Flyer* answered the controls sweetly. At fifty-nine seconds, by the Doctor's reckoning, the *Flyer* touched down safely. Wilbur raced up, yelling: 'Orv, the age of the flying machine is here!'

With the help of Tegan and Turlough, the brothers soon had the *Flyer* safely shut up in the makeshift hangar. Then they all repaired to the hut next door where, shivering with cold, they cooked up a hot meal of beans and brewed up sweet cocoa to thaw them all out.

Wilbur swigged his tin mug of cocoa in one. 'Anyone got a pencil and a scrap of paper?' Tegan calmly produced a plastic-backed notebook and a biro. Wilbur studied them carefully as he'd never seen such things in his life before! 'Say, where'd you get these, ma'am?' He wrote in the notebook and his eyes lit up. 'Wow! It's like a pencil but it writes like ink . . .' He tried to smudge what he had written. 'It doesn't smudge!' He turned to his brother. 'Gee, Orv, bet you wish you'd invented this! ma'am, you'll make a dollar or two out of this here ink-pencil!'

Tegan nodded demurely but didn't tell the brothers about the (later) commercial success of the Biro.

'Here!' Wilbur handed the notebook to his brother. 'What d'you think, Orv?'

Orville read out what his brother had written. 'It's a telegram to our father in Dayton, Ohio. It reads: *"Success! Four flights against wind with engine power alone. Average speed through air 31 miles an hour. Longest flight 59 seconds. Inform Press. Signed Wilbur and Orville."* That's grand, Wilbur, just grand.'

'I thought we'd get right down to the railhead, Orv, and send your telegram off by Morse telegraph to Dayton,' added Wilbur.

'In that case,' put in the Doctor, 'we won't keep you. A historic flight, gentlemen! If I may ask, how long has it taken you both to invent your flying machine?'

'Well, sir,' began Wilbur, 'we made our very first glider in August eighteen hundred and ninety-nine, eh Orv?' Orv nodded. 'This year we worked hard all through the long, hot summer on making a *light* petrol engine. Then there were the propellors, you see.' Wilbur scratched his head. 'Our kind didn't exist, so we just made them up, invented them.'

'Like longer, thinner ship's propellors, you get me?' Orville explained. 'We reckoned they would screw through the air just like a ship's propeller screws through water. That's why we put them to *push* the *Flyer*.'

'Ever thought of putting them in front?' the Doctor asked airily, 'So the prop *pulls* the aeroplane along?'

'Nope!' said Orville. 'But sounds like a mighty fine idea. Say, are you one of us doggoned inventors too, sir?'

Tegan broke in before the Doctor could make a modest reply, 'Why did you call your magnificent machine the *Flyer*?'

Orville looked almost bashful. 'We named it for our first little success story – a bicycle we designed back in Dayton.'

'We sold hundreds of that bicycle,' said Wilbur with a smile. 'Gave us the money to build our flying machine.'

'Very interesting!' said the Doctor. 'Well, we must be getting back now.'

'Pleasure to have known you, sir, ma'am . . .' They shook hands all round. 'And thanks for your help.'

As the trio marched over the dunes to the TARDIS, Tegan burst into song:

> 'Those daring young men
> in their flying machine,
> They flew through the air
> driven by gasoline.
>
> Those brothers, the Wrights,
> in a gale, oh so keen,
> They flew through the air
> in their *Flyer* machine.'

Her effort was greeted with mixed groans and cheers.

'Please Doctor,' Turlough pleaded once safely inside the TARDIS. 'A quiz, anything, to take Tegan's mind off composing . . .'

Aero Quiz

'Only eighty years ago,' said the Doctor, 'the first flight took place at Kitty Hawk. Yet today one airway alone can in a single year fly all the inhabitants of Manhattan across the Atlantic.'

'Suppose they wanted to stay put in New York, Doctor?' remarked Tegan cheekily.

Ignoring her, the Doctor began his first question.

1. 'The giant of all passenger and cargo planes is without doubt the Jumbo jet—' the Doctor began, but Tegan interrupted him with:

'I've air-hostessed on one of them!'

'Air-hostess with the mostest!' Turlough giggled.

'Ah, well,' the Doctor restored order. 'You'll be able to answer this one then, Tegan. How many times would the *Flyer* fit into the tail-plane of a Jumbo?'

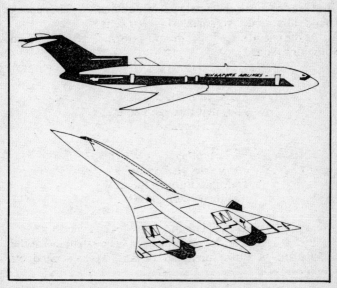

2. 'The *Flyer* went about as fast as a horse can run,' said the Doctor. 'That's about nineteen kilometres an hour, or 30 miles per hour. Well now, *Concorde* is the fastest thing on two wings – not counting military jets of course. It can go faster than a rifle bullet. And as we are all painfully aware, it can also break the sound barrier—'

'What's that?' piped up Tegan.

'You should know, Tegan!' guffawed Turlough.

'That's the speed of sound. Which is about 756 miles an hour, or 1200 kilometres an hour,' explained the Doctor. '*Concorde* can actually go at twice the speed of sound. So how many times faster than the *Flyer* can it fly?'

3. 'Fully loaded, the Jumbo jet weighs a shade over 300 tons,' said the Doctor. 'Now the *Flyer* weighed a mere 750 pounds, or 340 kilograms, complete with a one hundred kilogram engine and a pilot. So how many times heavier do you think a Jumbo jet is than the *Flyer*?'

'Depends what the pilot had for lunch!' Tegan laughed at her joke so much she nearly fell off her chair.

Super Paper Space-Dart!

'So much for going round the Earth,' said the Doctor. 'The next step was to get off it!'

'How'd they do that?' asked Turlough eagerly.

'Rockets!' said the Doctor. 'But, before we see the beginnings of space flight here's a paper dart you can make that's like a space craft of the future. The real one goes in space. The paper ones goes in air. Here's how you make it.'

The Doctor took a sheet of paper (A4). He folded it across a diagonal. Then he used a ruler to tear it neatly across the edge to make a square, its edge the same as the shorter edge of the sheet – 21 centimetres long and wide.

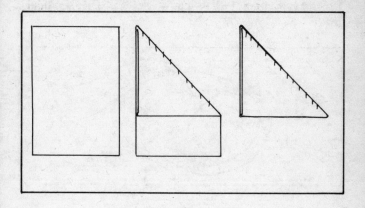

Then he explained the steps.

'First start at one of the corners not on the diagonal crease. Fold the corner in about a centimetre. Crease it. Fold again, and again, and again . . . a dozen or so times. That should get you to the diagonal. You should now have a triangle of paper, with a thick fold along its base.'

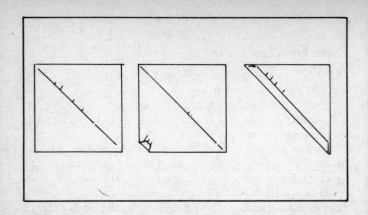

'Now curl the ends of the folded base together and slip one end of the base inside the other – you may need a drop of glue to hold it in place. You now have what looks like a bishop's mitre.'

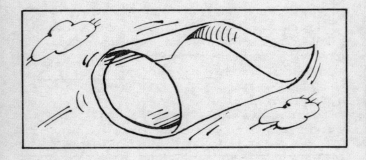

'Bishop's *what*?' chuckled Tegan. 'Might as well know!'

'Hat!' said the Doctor. 'Now, hold the paper space craft with the thick folded edge forwards and gently toss it into the air.'

Turlough found his sailed much further than any paper dart *he*'d ever made at school.

You make one and try it for yourself. It may be the space shape of the future.

The Russian Space Dreamer

'And now we come to the daddy of space-flight – on paper, that is,' the Doctor announced. 'He was a dreamer – a prophet of the shape of things to come. He built space ships of the mind.

'In 1903, you remember, the Wright brothers flew for the first time at Kitty Hawk. In that year this man worked out all the laws of space flight. The maths of it and all that.'

At the word 'maths' Tegan made one of her faces.

'He knew for sure that a rocket was the only way to get off the Earth—'

Tegan started to croon, 'Stop the Earth: I want to get off!'

The Doctor hurried on. 'He was born in 1857 and lived in the small town of Kaluga, a hundred miles south of Moscow—'

'He was a Russian, Doctor!' Turlough whooped.

'How did you guess?' the Doctor said sharply. 'He was also a deaf school teacher and as a lad, taught himself maths and physics. Then he got into aeronautics—'

'Airo- what, Doctor?' Tegan piped up.

'Nautics, Tegan,' the Doctor replied. 'It means the science of navigation in the sky.'

'So an astronaut,' Tegan said, 'is someone who navigates in space?'

'Right,' the Doctor beamed. 'Then our Russian got the space bug. By 1898 he'd got the maths of rockets licked. Did you know, all our space vehicle designs are based on his equations?'

Turlough looked very worried. 'I'll never make a space-man then, Doctor.'

'Why's that, Turlough?'

'Can't do algebra!' Turlough replied.

'Never mind, Turlough,' said the Doctor soothingly. 'It's all worked out for you. Anyway, while the Wright brothers

17

were making their first flights, this Russian was already writing about space-satellites, solar energy from the Sun, space-suits and even how to take a bath in space!'

'What, those funny showers, Doctor?' asked Tegan.

'Yes, those centrifugal showers space-men use. This Russian foresaw even *them*. He put all these theories in an amazing book, *Outside the Earth*. Know what? He even hit on the formula for working out the jet speed of the gases from a rocket. He also worked out how much fuel a rocket needs to put such-and-such a payload in space.'

'Quite a guy, Doctor!' Turlough said from where he lounged lazily in his chair.

'This Russian also thought out the multi-stage rocket. He called it a rocket-train,' said the Doctor. 'By the time he was seventy, he was a national hero in Russia. And, when he died in 1935, he was given a state funeral. Tell me, what's his name?'

'I know,' said Turlough, fetching a Vitamin Drink for

Tegan and himself from the TARDIS' cooler. 'You've said it, Doctor – Whatsisname!'

'Thank you Turlough, and good night!' said the Doctor crossly. Then he smiled. 'Look, I'll give you a clue. His name is an anagram of IVY SOKT SKOL!'

True to form Tegan had the last word. 'Good on yer, Ivy!' Then, raising her plastic cup, she called out cheerily, 'Skol!'

Back-garden Rocket

'Come with me,' said the Doctor in hushed tones, 'to an orchard near Worcester, in Massachusettes, America. Picture, if you will, a beautiful autumn day in New England. It is October the nineteenth, 1899. A seventeen-year-old high school kid has climbed a cherry tree. He looks down at the ground way below him. Suddenly he has a flash vision of a spacecraft that will carry man to the planet Mars. As he climbs out of the tree, he says to himself: 'I will make a Moon rocket!' And a year later to the day he climbed the same tree and—'

Turlough's hand shot up. 'I know, Doctor. He'd left something up the tree. I say, what's the matter, Doctor?'

'Nothing,' said the Doctor weakly when he could bring himself to speak. 'What I was going to say was, he made the same vow again. Oh, never mind . . . Now, the man in my last question, you remember, worked out all the rocket equations on paper. But this New England inventor made rockets that actually *flew*.'

'I know who he is,' Turlough tried once more. 'George Washington!'

'It couldn't have been, Turlough,' Tegan chipped in. 'George Washington cut the cherry tree *down*!' Turlough was most put out and brooded in silence.

'Now we've settled *that*,' croaked the Doctor, 'perhaps we can go on . . . This inventor chappie was a sickly boy but very clever. Often away from school through illness, he lapped up books like *The War of the Worlds* by H. G. Wells. It set him off dreaming about making rockets. Even as a University student he'd worked out that the best rocket fuel was liquid hydrogen and liquid oxygen. But in his day you couldn't buy them "off the shelf".'

Turlough's face lit up at the mention of chemicals.

'I rather liked "stinks" at school, Doctor.'

'As it happens, Turlough, our inventor liked *physics*,' the Doctor said drily. 'He was a physics prof at university. And he gave lectures on moon rockets. Then in 1920, he got a five thousand dollar grant to build test rockets. The newspapers poked fun at him – nicknamed him "Moon-Rocket Man" – and the neighbours were up in arms about the din his test rockets made.'

Turlough saw a chance to get his own back. 'Lucky they didn't have Tegan for a neighbour!'

'TEGAN!' the Doctor warned her before she could reply in kind. 'Our inventor used to make his tests on his Aunt Effie's farm. After one particularly loud test flight, ambulances, the police and journalists arrived at Aunt Effie's. Next day the newspapers carried this banner headline:

MOON ROCKET MISSES TARGET
BY 238,799½ MILES

'Doctor!' Turlough shot up his hand. 'Where was the target, then?'

'Oh, my Sainted Aunt Effie,' Tegan crowed happily. 'The *Moon*, you juggins!'

'Our poor inventor,' said the Doctor, 'was promptly banned from testing rockets in New England. He had to move his operations to a marsh, miles from anywhere, called Hell Pond. To save money he bought secondhand machinery from the local farmers. He used an old metal frame windmill for a launch tower. His rockets weren't much taller than a man, remember. And they didn't have shiny smooth cigar cases like today's giant Saturn V rocket. They were just an open mesh of slim rods and metal tubes filled with fuels. These had to be stuck out front, well away from the engine at the back.'

'How high did they go, Doctor?' Tegan asked.

'Oh, his very first rocket only got up to 184 feet, Tegan,' said the Doctor. 'The flight time was a bare two and a half seconds. Our intrepid inventor had to light the rocket with a blowlamp. It was early spring, with snow still thick on the ground.'

'Where did it land, Doctor?' asked Tegan, all agog.

The Doctor chuckled, 'In Aunt Effie's cabbage patch! But you mustn't run away with the idea that he was a duffer.

'The amazing thing was, this inventor had built a perfect twenty-two-foot rocket by 1940. That was two years before the Germans launched their first V-2 rocket. In 1945 our inventor saw a captured V-2. Apart from being bigger than his rocket, it was almost exactly the same! After the War, the German rocket experts all agreed that the American rocketeer was "ahead of us all".

'Now, do you know his name?'

Whiz-Bangs and Rockets Quiz

It had been a busy morning what with the controls and micros to check for the coming trip to the planets. So it seemed to the Doctor a good time to brush up on their knowledge of how you get off this Earth and into space. 'Programming the grey cells,' the Doctor called it, although with Tegan it was more a case of 'reprogramming' rather than 'programming'

The Doctor flung his straw Panama hat on the wooden Victorian hatstand to gain their attention.

'Shot!' Turlough called out as if he were back on the cricket field of his old school.

'Fluke, more like,' Tegan chortled in her down under Aussie way. 'Either way it means a quiz.'

1. 'First question,' said the Doctor. 'Right up your street, Tegan! It's to do with films. Who invented the count-down?'

'Five-four-three-two-one-BLAST OFF!' Turlough called out from his corner.

'Don't be rude,' Tegan flung back. 'I know, a mathematician who was still learning to count!'

'Sounds like the sort of maths masters I had,' said Turlough.

Well, can *you* guess who invented the count-down?

2. 'As you chaps all know,' began the Doctor, 'the conquest of space was made by—'

'Got it – rockets!' yelled Tegan.

'Quite,' said the Doctor testily. 'But that's not the question, Tegan. The question is – who designed the first incendiary rockets?'

'What does *incendiary* mean?' asked Tegan.

Turlough shot up his hand. 'Burning, doesn't it Doctor?'

'Y-e-es,' said the Doctor grudgingly. 'What it really means

is "for the purpose of setting houses and so forth alight".'

'Like the incendiary bombs during the War, Doctor?' asked Turlough.

'Exactly,' said the Doctor. 'And here's a hint: the same people invented gunpowder.'

3. 'At the capture of Baghdad in 1258, the Mongols used rockets against the Arabs, who called them "Arrows from Cathay" – that's the old, poetic name for China. The Indians were next to use rockets, to devastating effect, at the battles of Seringapatam in 1792 and 1799 against the British. So one of the British soldiers, an engineer, decided to pinch the idea. He designed a bigger and better incendiary rocket. It weighed fourteen and a half kilograms – about thirty-two pounds – and had a range of some three thousand metres – just shy of two miles! Did you know Nelson, the famous British admiral—'

'We *know* who Nelson was, Doctor,' Tegan sniffed.

'Nelson used these rockets to blow the Danish ships out of the Baltic Sea in the Battle of Copenhagen in 1801, which he went on to win. These rockets were used again when the British blockaded American ships in the ridiculous War of 1812 – well, all wars are absurd, aren't they? The whole thing was an awful mistake. That's what's meant by 'the rocket's red glare' in the American national anthem "The Star-Spangled Banner".'

'You're a positive mine of information,' Tegan chuckled at her pun.

'There was only one trouble with these rockets; they needed long sticks to steady them, like firework rockets. What was the name of the British soldier who invented them?'

4. 'The next stage in rocket design was to do away with the stick,' declared the Doctor. 'An Englishman improved military rockets by drilling angled vents around the base so that the gases from the gunpowder shot out through the vents and spun the rockets round. This spin steadied the rockets in flight. Then he added curved vanes, much like the tail of a giant space rocket today, which made the rockets spin . . .'

Tegan had begun to fidget. 'Don't know about you, but my *head* is spinning. All these facts . . .'

'Jolly interesting, though, Doctor,' said Turlough.

'Teacher's pet!' Tegan shot back at Turlough.

'Anyway,' said the Doctor, ignoring them. 'Do you know who improved the rocket in this way?'

5. 'The first practical rocket ever made was, I'm sad to say,' began the Doctor, 'the German V-2 rocket, used to bomb London in World War Two. The first successful V-2 flight broke all records for height, weight, speed and range. It took place on October the third, 1942.

'That first V-2 went 190 kilometres and reached a staggering height of eighty-five kilometres – well above the Earth's atmosphere. It also broke the sound barrier,' the Doctor told them. 'But it also took another two years to have it ready to bomb London.'

Then the Doctor added dreamily: 'The V-2 launch was, you know, a "high" in space flight. An amazing high-technology breakthrough.

'Do you know where the launch pads were? It was somewhere in Holland . . .'

6. 'Dash it!' cried the Doctor, 'I clean forgot to ask you the name of the German who made the V-2 rocket. . . . Tell me, what was his name?'

'Oh,' said Turlough, 'I was going to ask *you* that, Doctor.'

'Go on, Doctor,' wheedled Tegan. 'Give us a clue!'

'Well, all right, Tegan,' the Doctor gave way to her. 'I'll tell you something that happened to him during the War. Even though he worked for the Nazis, it shows he wasn't such a bad chap after all. The first V-2 was launched in Holland in 1942. Our man in Holland had to work two more years on the V-2 before it was ready to fire at London. Then in March 1944, the much-hated secret police, the Gestapo, arrested him. They feared he might nip over to the British

side with all his rocket secrets. He didn't help his case when he told the Gestapo: "The V-2 isn't a war weapon. I had space travel in mind when I built it. I'm sorry it's to be used as a weapon." Worse still, the Gestapo suspected he wasn't interested in building the Thousand-Year-Reich! For the Gestapo wanted Nazi Germany, the Reich, to last for a thousand years. Luckily for him, a famous German General got him out of prison.'

'Phew!' Turlough gasped, 'a pretty close shave, Doctor!'

Big Bang, Black Holes and Planets

After breakfast, Tegan, still chewing, asked, 'About that trip round the planets, Doctor . . . you did promise!'

'I've already programmed the Time Console for it,' replied the Doctor, adding sharply, 'while you were still in bed! I've got a great ten thousand million years lined up for you and Turlough.'

Turlough looked up from his cup of tea. 'That long, Doctor?'

''Fraid so,' said the Doctor. 'That's how long ago the creation of the Universe was – the Big Bang.'

'Big Bang, Doctor?' asked Turlough. 'Hope it's loud enough for you, Tegan! And will we meet life on other worlds, Doctor?'

'Wait and see!' answered the Doctor mysteriously. 'First, our own Solar System.'

Tegan's eyebrows shot up in query, 'That means our Sun System?'

The Doctor nodded and he hit the 'Run' key on the TARDIS video. A picture flashed up on the screen of the Earth in a jet black sky rushing towards them. It zoomed in first on Europe, then Britain, then London, and finally on the City of London. Centre-screen they saw the dome of St Paul's Cathedral gleaming in the sunlight. Suddenly it changed to a great ball of fire.

'There!' said the Doctor proudly. 'The Sun! Cut down to size. Now watch! You'll see the Earth and other planets scaled down to match this midget Sun, all with their distances on the same scale. Just a little video I edited last night,' he added modestly.

The picture tracked away westwards from St Paul's Sundome. A couple of blocks away it paused and zoomed in on a tiny ping-pong ball in Queen Victoria Street.

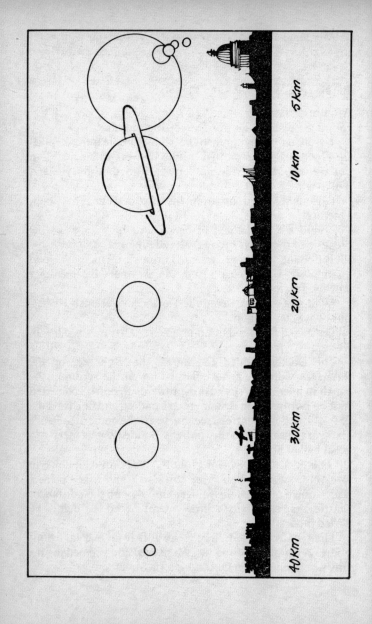

5km

10km

20km

30km

40km

'Mercury!' boomed the Doctor. 'Micro-mercury, rather – the smallest of the planets. We're now about 400 metres from St Paul's. Call it half a kilometre.'

The camera moved along Queen Victoria Street and froze at the Mermaid Theatre in Puddle Dock. Outside it was a large, juicy orange.

'Food for thought!' chortled Tegan.

'Venus, actually,' said the Doctor drily, 'on my scale of things. We're now 700 metres from the Cathedral.'

The camera tracked on to Blackfriars Bridge, where it zoomed in on a big, yellow grapefruit.

'More food for thought, Tegan!' the Doctor got in first. 'The Earth! On our London-sized solar system! We're now one kilometre from St Paul's.'

Further on, the picture zoomed in on a snooker ball lying on Waterloo Bridge.

'We are one and a half kilometres from St Paul's and that's Mars.'

The camera zoomed out again and whizzed over Horse-guard's Parade and Whitehall, along the Mall, over Buckingham Palace and on to Sloane Square. The Doctor hit the 'freeze-frame' key and 'zoom-in' and they saw, sitting outside Sloane Square Underground Station, a big red beach ball.

'Like the colour?' asked the Doctor. 'I chose it to match Jupiter's famous Red Spot. It is just over a metre across. We're now five kilometres away from St Paul's.'

The Doctor hit the 'run' key and the picture snaked along the Thames to Hammersmith Bridge where it zoomed in on a medicine ball, a shade smaller than the Sloane Square beach ball, and with flattened hoops round it. 'What do you think of my Saturn, chaps?' asked the Doctor. 'The next biggest planet. On my London scale it's ten kilometres from my St Paul's Sun.'

The next freeze-frame showed a big Japanese paper lamp-shade, a ball 37 centimetres across, lost in Hampton Court Maze.

'Uranus,' said the Doctor. 'Twenty kilometres out.'

The next stop action picture was on the far westerly runway of Heathrow Airport of a slightly smaller 'ball' lampshade. 'Thirty-five centimetres across,' said the Doctor. 'That's Neptune. Thirty kilometres out.'

Lastly the camera homed in on a golf ball in Windsor Great Park, beyond the Castle.

'Lost in the rough!' the Doctor chuckled briefly. 'Pluto! Forty kilometres from St Paul's.'

'Gee,' whooped Tegan, 'that's great!'

'I agree,' said the Doctor modestly. 'But wait! The planets aren't stuck in one place all the time. That's how they got their name: *planet* means *wanderer*. Nor do they wander, really. They *hurtle* through space. In giant orbits. Pretty nearly circles, but not quite. Ovals really.'

'Egg-shapes, you mean, Doctor?' quizzed Turlough.

Tegan pealed with laughter. 'Hark at old egg-head.'

'Oh, they're not as flattened as *that*,' said the Doctor briskly. 'Indeed, Mercury and Pluto are the only planets that move in obvious ovals. The others are more like circles.'

'How fast do they go then, Doctor?' asked Turlough.

'Well, the Earth cracks on at eighteen and a half miles a second. Call it twenty miles a second. That's the distance from St Paul's to Hampton Court in one second flat. Nearly seventy thousand miles an hour.'

'The planets go as fast as *that*?' gasped Tegan.

'Nearer the Sun they go faster still!' said the Doctor.

'Hang on, Doctor!' said Turlough, grappling with this new idea. 'Pluto's farthest away from the Sun. Right? So it goes the slowest.'

'Right, Turlough!' the Doctor beamed at his 'star' pupil. 'You'd better take a rest after that mental leap. Yes, Pluto crawls round at a mere three miles a second. Or eleven thousand miles an hour. Then Neptune's faster still. And Saturn goes twice as fast as Pluto. Jupiter goes eight miles a second, Mars zooms round at twice that speed. Venus is a bit faster than the Earth with Mercury, closest to the Sun, the winner at thirty miles a second.'

'I must say, it never felt as speedy-Gonzalez as that when I was at school on Earth!' said Turlough, puzzled.

'No, we don't feel it,' said the Doctor. 'Not on Earth. Don't forget the Earth is turning as well. So a chap on the Equator is whizzing on a giant roundabout at a mere one thousand miles per hour. On top of that our whole galaxy – the Solar System – is turning at 8000 mph. Then to cap it all, they've recently discovered that our galaxy is falling through space. Gently, that is, for a galaxy! It's slipping towards a denser part of the Universe at 20,000 mph.'

'Makes my head spin!' croaked Tegan. 'Can we go and see how it all began now?'

The Doctor programmed the TARDIS' Time Console for their Ultimate Trip. 'We're off to see the creation of the Universe, chaps!' he called out cheerily. 'What you're going to see is the Big Bang itself. I've tapped onto a light beam that has been trapped for 10,000 million years in a Black Hole. By a trick of gravity waves I've managed to release the light beam. That's what we're seeing . . . on our screen NOW! Just a case of looking back in time – down a light beam!'

On screen they saw a *ginormous* explosion. The temperature gauge showed billions of degrees as the TARDIS' Super-Clock of Ages ticked away through one million years. The tiny ball of a Universe got bigger and bigger – a great fireball of heat and light – before their very eyes. Then, over the next few millions of years, by the Super-Clock, the gases that were swirling about in the Universe began to cool.

The Doctor commentated for them: 'First atoms forming now.'

'Atoms, Doctor?' enquired Turlough.

'Smallest components of chemical elements,' said the Doctor watching the screen. He switched on the Electron Microscope. 'Look, there they are! Hydrogen and helium!' They were treated to a mighty close-up of the actual atoms forming.

'Hey! See that!' the Doctor leaned forward excitedly as

millions of years ticked by on the Super-Clock. 'The first stars forming! That's the work of gravity. Pulling together the dust and gas flying through space.'

'So that's how the Signs of the Zodiac got made!' whooped Tegan. 'Look at that fried egg! Or is it a squashed UFO? I bet that's your sign, Turlough!'

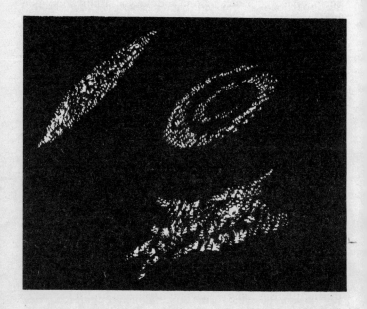

Before Turlough could lam out at her, the Doctor cooled it with: 'Actually, Tegan, the galaxy you are referring to is our very own – the Solar System. And it's not a fried egg, it's a spiral. You can see two other types of galaxy too – elliptical (that means oval), and plain old irregular.

'The Milky Way, Turlough,' the Doctor turned to him, 'is what we on Earth see of our own galaxy, looked at through the thickest part.'

'It's too much, Doctor,' said Tegan, making for the TARDIS' foodstore. 'Galaxy, Milky Way, fried eggs . . . must have something to eat!'

'Remember the Sun and its planets are just a tiny part of our galaxy,' the Doctor continued unabashed. 'We are not at the centre but out towards the edge. Imagine some specks of pepper shaken on the white of a fried egg, near its rim. Well, the pepper is the Solar System and the yolk is the Milky Way in our galaxy.'

Tegan came back munching a gooey chocolate-covered bar. 'Helps me work, rest and play, Doctor!'

'Just telling Turlough about fried eggs,' said the Doctor absent-mindedly, still eyeing the screen.

Tegan shot the Doctor a puzzled look, but he pointed excitedly at the screen. They saw swirls of bright pin-pricks of light spiralling into a central black hole and vanishing.

'Mini black holes!' said the Doctor. 'They formed soon after the Big Bang – well, a few million years after, that is. Extraordinary thing about them is, they've got the mass of a big mountain packed into the tiny space of an atom!'

'And that mountain of stellar stuff will never see the light of day, never ever?' sighed Tegan sadly.

'It shouldn't,' said the Doctor quite worked up now, 'but it *does*. In dribs and drabs. You see, mini black holes are leaky. They leak energy and sometimes explode. So if they discovered any mini black holes in space, then they'd know the Big Bang really happened. Because mini's only formed during the Big Bang. They are hoping to find some mini's with the help of the Space Shuttle one day.'

'Doctor, look at the Super-Clock. It's registering five thousand million years ago now!' Turlough called out.

'By Jove, doesn't time fly when you're talking,' joked the Doctor.

'You mean, when *you* are, Doctor!' Tegan quipped back.

'Five thousand million years ago. Time the Solar System was made!' the Doctor announced like a Master Chef cooking a great feast. And, sure enough, on screen they saw the Sun, followed by its nine planets, form out of a swirling mass of billowing clouds of dust and gas.

'Boring!!' yelled Tegan, hitting the Fast Forward key. The Super-Clock raced forward millions and millions of years in a matter of seconds. The Doctor reached over and hit the Slow-Mo key. The Super-Clock slowed, quite by chance, at the year AD 1054. On screen was a fantastic splash of light. Gas and dust was spraying out from a socking great explosion in the sky.

'Nice timing, Tegan,' the Doctor beamed. 'The most famous Supernova ever seen by man – ordinary man, that is.' He coughed modestly.

'It terrified the life out of the Chinese in 1054,' the Doctor went on. 'It was visible even in daylight for two years! They called it the Crab Nebula – the Crab Cloud – because of its crabby shape.'

'Not the only crabby one round here,' Tegan muttered gleefully.

The Doctor ignored her. 'It's still spraying out radio waves like a broadcasting station gone berserk.' He hit another key. 'Now for that mystery tour of the planets! We'll start next door to the Sun, at Mercury!'

The screen changed instantly to pictures of Mercury's surface, pitted with vast craters.

'Remember the photos taken in 1974 by the space probe, Mariner 10?' remarked the Doctor. 'It's not unlike the Moon, and the biggest crater, the Caloris Basin, is as big as France, Germany and Italy put together!'

'What's it like out there, Doctor?' asked Turlough.

'No air,' said the Doctor. 'Jolly hot in the long days and well below zero at night.' He hit the Space Move key and up came a picture of a planet seen from afar, covered in swirling cloud. Great flashes of lightning rent the clouds.

'Venus!' announced the Doctor. 'That cloud cools to an acid rain. Sulphuric acid.'

'Nasty!' said Tegan. 'But I thought it was meant to have life on it?'

'No chance,' said the Doctor, 'It's like a hothouse for one thing. The Sun's heat gets trapped inside the clouds, like a greenhouse, whizzing the temperature up to 500°C; more like a roasting oven.'

'What's the other thing?' asked Turlough.

'The pressure at ground level is so great that the first space probes, Venera 9 and 10, were crushed in a few minutes. That's the bad news. And the good news: the atmosphere round it is almost pure carbon dioxide – you know, like the fizzy in lemonade – and so if we could drop micro-bugs from a rocket, they would eat up the fizzy and give out oxygen. The clouds would clear and the heat get less. But that's just a pipe-dream so far. Next planet!'

The Doctor hit the Space Move key again, leaving out the Earth, and up came a picture of Mars.

'Old hat!' shouted Tegan. 'We saw the pictures on telly yonks ago!'

'Two Viking space probes landed on Mars in 1976, as you know, Turlough,' lectured the Doctor. 'Alas, they found no real signs of life on Mars. Volcanoes, yes, once highly active. Most interestingly, they found dried-up river beds. Perhaps rivers once flowed there. Even now vast pockets of water may lurk deep underground.'

'What about those red canals, Doctor?' asked Turlough. 'We used to lead our "stinks" master off on red herrings about them – to get him off boring old chemmy formulas.'

'Oh, astronomers once swore they could see straight lines of canals on Mars,' said the Doctor. 'They thought they were made by intelligent beings. But, alas, there are no canals. They simply imagined them!'

'What's it like on Mars, Doctor?' asked Tegan.

'The same day and night as on Earth,' said the Doctor. 'It's mostly red-rust desert. The thin air is pretty well all carbon dioxide and it's always thirty degrees below. Freezing!'

The Doctor hit the Space Move key and the screen showed

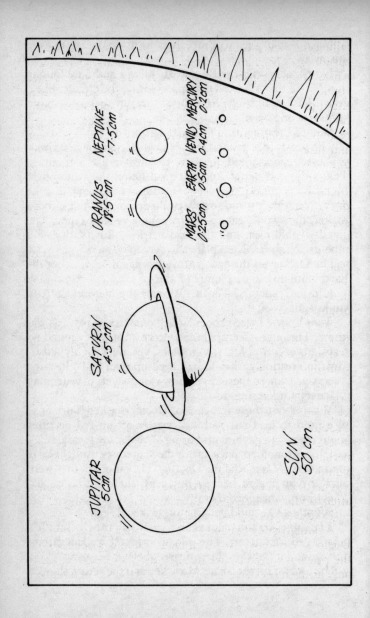

falling stars and a fiery-tailed comet. 'Asteroids!' the Doctor called out. 'They and meteors, or falling stars, and comets whizz through space between Mars and the next planet coming up, Jupiter. Meteors are tiny grains of dust. When they hit the Earth's atmosphere they get hot and glow. That's how we see them – as falling or shooting stars. Comets are really giant snowballs. Their head is rock and frozen water and ammonia gas. Their tails, made of dust and gas, may be millions of kilometres long!'

'Isn't there a Halley's Comet, Doctor?' Turlough quizzed.

'There is, indeed, Turlough,' said the Doctor. 'Halley's is the best known. It orbits the Sun and returns to our skies every seventy-six years. It came by last in 1910. Of course, there are lots of others.'

The next planet to come up on screen was big Jupiter. 'Any bigger,' said the Doctor, 'and it would have become a star. Then its sheer size would have been enough to make a nuclear reactor of its heart. And then it would have shone brightly – as a star or sun.'

'What's that Red Spot on it, Doctor?' asked Turlough. 'Like the one on the beach ball in Sloane Square.'

'Probably a giant storm on its surface,' said the Doctor, 'which is a mass of swirling freezing ammonia. The Red Spot is bigger than the Earth! Under the clouds is a cool sea of liquid hydrogen. Thunder and lightning storms rage all day long. But all the ingredients for making life are there.'

'And anywhere else, Doctor?' Tegan pressed him.

'On Europa, one of Jupiter's fourteen moons, yes . . . perhaps. But it's a big perhaps. Jupiter would be a wonderful sight to see from one of her moons.'

The next video showed Saturn, the next biggest planet after Jupiter, with its beautiful pair of flat rings round it.

'Like a flattened halo!' chuckled Tegan.

'A double halo of pebbles and snowballs, Tegan,' said the Doctor. 'We know that from radar soundings bounced off the rings. They are wafer thin, by the way: ten kilometres only at the most. The outer ring is over a sixth of a million

kilometres in diameter! The same as half the distance between the Earth and the Moon. We don't know how the double rings were formed. Probably rubbish and bits from a moon shattered by gravity.'

'Any chance of life on it?' asked Turlough hopefully.

'None at all, old chap,' said the Doctor. 'Most unfriendly, gassy, cold, and mostly made of liquid hydrogen. Next slide!' The Doctor showed the last, outer three planets in quick succession.

'The last planets, farthest from the Sun!' said the Doctor, 'Not much to say about them, really. Uranus and Neptune are giant balls of gas. Uranus has five rings, not two like Saturn. It is covered by a layer of methane gas.'

'What, marsh gas, Doctor?' asked Turlough. 'I remember old "stinks" used to light test tubes of it. Burnt with a blue flame. Will-o'-the-wisp, he called it.'

'The very same gas, Turlough!' said the Doctor. 'Neptune is famous for one thing: it was found by maths!' Tegan made a 'yuk' face. 'Yes, two mathematician chappies predicted where it would be. When the astronomers looked through their spy-glasses in the direction calculated by the mathematicians, they saw Neptune. On target!'

'What about Pluto?' asked Turlough.

'Not discovered until 1930,' said the Doctor. 'So cold it's almost the lowest temperature it's possible to get: absolute zero. Don't know what it's made of, probably ice. One thing puzzles astronomers about it.'

'What's that?' asked Tegan.

'Its orbit is off-kilter. The orbits of all the other planets lie in one flat layer of space. But not Pluto. As a result it crosses Neptune's orbit. But, don't worry, they're not going to crash! And another thing: it's so far out, to someone on Pluto the Sun would be just a bright star among many, many others.'

'So no life anywhere in our Solar System, then,' said Turlough sadly.

'We mustn't give up hope,' replied the Doctor. 'None in

our System but there are thousands of other suns in our galaxy, each with their planets. On one or more of them there may be advanced civilisations. And that's only in our galaxy. Which is only a small part of the whole Universe.'

'Do you think Earthlings will ever go to live in space, Doctor?' Tegan asked perkily.

'Let's take a look!' said the Doctor, reprogramming the TARDIS' Time Console. 'Just as I said, Turlough!' he added mysteriously.

In no time they found the TARDIS was floating towards a spaceship of a sort no one has ever seen. But then, as the Super-Clock showed, it was the year AD 2111.

'Wow,' yelled Tegan as she saw it on their Intruder Screen. 'Look at that silver tube, Turlough!'

'*Ginormous!*' Turlough whistled. 'As thick as the length of a rugger pitch!'

'And two miles long,' added the Doctor, eyeing the Length Scanner Grid he had superimposed on the screen. 'Guess what it is?'

'I know!' Turlough's voice riochetted round the Control Room. 'It's a Space Colony!'

The Doctor nodded happily. 'Told you we'd find life in space. There must be at least a hundred thousand people in that cylinder. They used the Space Shuttle from Earth to start building it, years ago.'

'Why's it spinning, Doctor?' asked Tegan impatiently.

'To give them G, Tegan,' chuckled the Doctor. 'Gravity! You know, just like when you spin a bucket of water round your head – *please* don't try it! – the water stays in. Swinging the bucket provides G for the water.'

'And those dark and clear stripes along the cylinder, Doctor?' Turlough looked puzzled. 'What are they?'

'Strips of window and land,' replied the Doctor. 'A window, then land, window-land-window, and so on, all round the cylinder. The windows let in sunlight – you note how the cylinder points lengthwise towards the Sun?'

Tegan suddenly let out a howl like a Dingo dog.

42

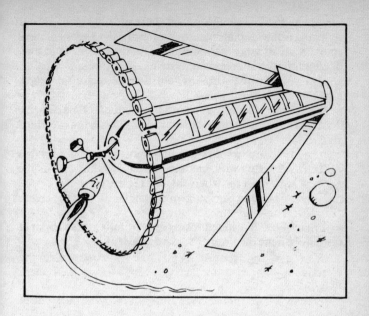

'Didgeridoo, Doctor! What's *that*?' She pointed a quivering finger at the Intruder Screen. Coming into view was a bullet-shaped spacecraft. It whizzed past the length of the cylinder, circled, then shot into the open end.

'Moonstuff!' the Doctor called out over his shoulder to them. 'It'll be chock-full of moon dust and rocks. They smelt it inside there' – he pointed to the middle of the cylinder – 'and turn it into useful metals. That's how they build on to their space colony. Then they don't have to go back down to Earth and overcome its gravity, which is very costly.'

The Doctor stood up. 'Seen enough?' he asked and switched off the screen. 'Never know, but those may be the only Earthlings left in the Universe, if . . .'

43

'If, Doctor?' Turlough looked shocked.

'If they blow themselves up on Earth,' the Doctor smiled ruefully. 'Tell you what. We could send a message out into deep space – to other solar systems – and see if we get an answer. Meanwhile what do you think of this little ditty I made up?'

While the Doctor reprogrammed the TARDIS, he declaimed, like an actor, these lines:

> 'Go and watch a falling star,
> Catch with lens a light beam ray.
> Show me where all past years are,
> Or the Big Bang on display.'

Tegan and Turlough clapped dutifully. The Doctor bowed, 'All me own work,' he said modestly.

The Planets Quiz

'Don't see why I shouldn't quiz you, do you?' said the Doctor the day after they finished their trip round the planets. Before either Tegan or Turlough could think of an answer the Doctor launched into the first question.

1. 'How long ago was the Big Bang?' he began.

2. 'On my London-sized solar system,' said the Doctor slotting in the video he had made for his companions and letting the video display run once more, 'you doubtless saw that most of my little planet models were a nice round number of kilometres from St Paul's – my model of the Sun.'

'I do believe I do,' Turlough said, desperately playing for time.

'Oh, yes, my lovely grapefruit – er, the Earth, I mean,' said Tegan, 'was a kilometre away from St Paul's. Right?'

'Just so,' said the Doctor. 'Now if you check over the video again' – and you, dear Reader, glance through the last chapter again – 'you should be able to jot down the distances in round numbers of kilometres of my model planets from St Paul's. Puzzle: The real distance in space of the grapefruit Earth from St Paul's Sun is 100 thousand miles. So can you say how far each of the other eight planets is from the Sun?'

'Lummy!' said Turlough. 'One kilometre becomes a hundred thousand miles. Which key do I press on my pocket calculator, Doctor?'

'My head's in a whirl already!' said Tegan.

Can *you* help them out?

3. 'You doubtless recall,' said the Doctor, 'the beach ball in Sloane Square and the grapefruit on Waterloo Bridge – on my London-sized solar system. I'll tell you now, the Earth is

8000 miles in diameter – that is, across at the Equator. So how big is Jupiter?'

4. The Doctor stood rocking on his heels, jingling coins in his pocket, the very picture of the Terror of the Lower Remove. 'Who first said the Sun, and not the Earth, is the centre of the universe?'

Turlough's hand shot up, 'You don't mean the chap who chucked cannon balls off the top of the Leaning Tower of Pisa, do you, Doc . . . er, Doctor?'

'No, Turlough, I was not actually thinking of Galileo, if that is who you mean.' Turlough nodded, crestfallen. Then his face brightened.

'Sir, *sir* – I mean Doctor – I know!'

'Yes, Turlough?'

'Copper Knickers, sir!' Tegan guffawed loud enough to wake all the 'roos in the Outback. The Doctor shot her a steely look.

'Thank you, Turlough, for that most enlightening piece of information. Nevertheless, he was a Pole. And he had a Latin name, ending in – *us*.'

Well, who was he? If you repeat very quickly what Turlough said it will sound like his real name.

'And now some quickies!' the Doctor promised. 'You can work them out by re-running my video of the London-sized solar system.'

5. 'How fast does Mars go round the Sun?'

6. 'Which planet goes round the Sun the fastest? Is it the planet nearest in to the Sun or farthest out?'

7. 'Which is the hottest planet? Is it nearest the Sun or farthest away?

8. 'Which are the four big planets?'

9. 'Which planet has all the ingredients for life on it?'

10. 'What is a meteor?'

11. 'And one for you to work out! When will Halley's comet come round the Earth next – if it is on time?'

The Message-in-a-bottle Puzzle

The Doctor strode spryly into the TARDIS' Console Room. He waved a sheet of paper at Tegan and Turlough who were chatting idly.

'Anyone like to send a message to E.T.? Well, here's how.'

The Doctor laid the sheet of paper on the table and took a pencil out of the breast pocket of his cream blazer. 'We'll soon see if there really *is* life in outer space.'

Tegan looked over the Doctor's shoulder. 'Going to send a message in a bottle, Doctor?'

'Sort of. A picture, actually, Tegan,' said the Doctor. 'Now, what is the best way to send it? I'd say as a row of 1s and 0s – like ONS and OFFS, dashes and dots, Yeses and Noes. In a nutshell, in binary.'

'Oh, painting by numbers, you mean, Doctor!' Tegan quipped.

'What are you going to send a picture *of*, Doctor?' Turlough blithely asked.

'Good question, Turlough!' the Doctor beamed. 'What do you suggest?'

'One of us, Doctor?' Turlough suggested.

'Don't send a snap of *him*, Doctor, whatever you do,' Tegan chuckled, ignoring Turlough's icy glare, 'or we'll never hear from poor E.T. again!'

''Fraid it'll have to be very, very simple, Tegan,' the Doctor muttered, already jotting some figures down.

'Oh, well, in that case, *do* send a picture of him!' Tegan fell about at her little joke. Turlough couldn't see what was so funny and he snapped at her, peevishly, 'Ha-jolly-ha!'

'By now the Doctor had jotted down these strange figures:

$$381 = 101111101$$
$$427 = 110101011$$
$$455 = 111000111$$

He held the sheet of paper up for all to see.

'I get it, Doctor! On the left you've written numbers the way we count, and on the right are the same numbers in binary. So the top line means three hundred and eighty one is equal to the top row of ones and zero's.' Turlough said triumphantly.

'Well done,' the Doctor went on, 'I'm going to send a message made up of ordinary three-figure numbers. Then this E.T. in outer space, when he gets my message, all he has to do is jot my numbers down in binary one beneath the other. Each binary number is a row of nine 1s and 0s. Set them down under each other and you'll get eight of these rows. Then pencil in the 0s to make them blacker. Forget about the 1s, or rub them out, and the blackened 0s show up as . . . as picture!'

'Cor, let me try!' Tegan shouted with glee.

'Hang on, Tegan!' The Doctor held up his hand. 'First let

me finish the message. *Then* you can change the numbers into binary. Get the picture? If you see what I mean!'

'Oh dear,' Tegan looked crestfallen. 'How do you do that?'

The Doctor put the sheet of paper on the table and pencilled in some more numbers. When he'd finished, the message looked like this:

$$381$$
$$427$$
$$455$$
$$455$$
$$455$$
$$439$$
$$439$$
$$439$$

'Is that all?' Tegan's face fell.

'It is,' said the Doctor easily. Then his face lit up. 'I say, chaps, if I give you the binary for 439, you don't need to do *any* heavy maths, do you? Oh, how stupid of me!' the Doctor added, writing '439 = 110111101' on the sheet of paper. 'Can't think why I didn't see it before . . .'

'Easily done!' said Turlough to the Doctor's intense irritation.

Why don't you try decoding the Doctor's space message? Follow the Doctor's instructions. Fill in the os, and see what the picture reminds you of.

Puzzle Messages

The Doctor had scribbled down these lists of binary numbers:

A 100111111, 110101011, 110000001, 111000000,
  111011101, 111011101.

B 10011011, 11010001, 11000000, 11100001, 11101101,
  11101101.

C 1001001001, 1000000001, 1000000001, 1000010001,
  1000111001, 1000111001.

D 110111111, 100011110, 111000001, 111000001,
  111011101.

The Doctor explained, 'All the numbers on my lists are in binary. So you don't have to change them. Write *them* in rows, of 1s and 0s, one under each other – just as I did before. Best to do it on squared paper. Blacken the 0s. And you should see the picture the E.T. will get. All you have to do then is say what it looks like.'

See what you can make of the Doctor's E.T. messages.

Starry Puzzlers

'Listen! A couple of funny puzzlers – about stars and planets,' the Doctor said brightly. 'They make jolly good party questions . . .'

'What parties do you go to, Doctor?' quipped Tegan.

'I mean to say, not a bit stuffy or 'heavy' – as you'd say, Tegan.'

'Say no more, Doctor!' said Tegan. But, of course, she knew he would. And he did. 'Here we go, then!' the Doctor went on.

1. 'O, Be a Fine Girl: Kiss Me!' the Doctor sang in a light bathroom tenor.

'Really, Doctor!' Tegan tried to look shocked.

The Doctor raced on. 'What would the words of my little song mean to a real stargazer?'

Turlough said excitedly, 'I think I know, Doctor: O for Orion. Am I on the right track?'

'Yes, on the right star track, Turlough,' said the Doctor, 'but don't give it away or you'll spoil it for Tegan.'

'Fat chance of that!' said Tegan flatly. 'Haven't the foggiest what you're on about, Doctor . . .'

'Dimmo!' Turlough teased Tegan. Then he said to the Doctor, 'Your "star" pupil's not very bright this morning, is she?'

'As usual, Turlough,' beamed the Doctor, 'you've unwittingly given us a brilliant clue – about dimness!'

'Or a dim clue about brightness,' Tegan added gaily.

Do *you* know what the Doctor's 'song' is about?

2. 'This should be up your street, Tegan,' the Doctor laughed. 'As you know, I think astrology is for the bards.' The Doctor really laughed this time – alone!

'Don't you mean "birds", Doctor?' asked Turlough.

'Oh, never mind!' said the Doctor. 'Anyway, astronomers use the same signs of the zodiac for the planets. Now, can you tell me what planet each of these signs stands for?' The Doctor drew these signs on the TARDIS' Micro Screen with the touch-sensitive pen:

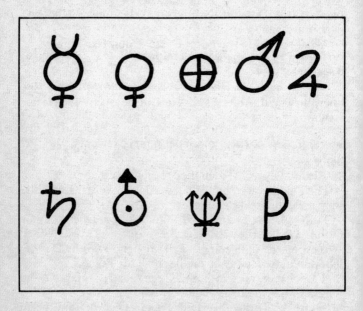

Do you know which planets these signs stand for?

Girl on the Moon

'Before I ask you a little quiz about the moon shots,' said the Doctor, 'why don't we make our own trip through space and have a good look at it?'

'Good idea, Doctor!' whooped Tegan. 'I've always wanted to see the other side.'

'And so we shall,' said the Doctor, programming the TARDIS to lift off and orbit the Moon.

In no time to speak of Turlough was looking out of a special porthole for viewing the outside world. 'Gosh, Doctor, there's some machinery down there!' And he pointed to the Moon's surface. On it they could just make out spidery legs and a metal platform.

Looking over his shoulder, Tegan yelled in his ear, 'the lunar module!' Turning, she added, 'Let's drop down and see it.'

'If we do, Tegan,' said the Doctor drily as he programmed the TARDIS to descend, 'the place will no longer deserve its name!'

'What do you mean, Doctor?' she asked.

'It won't be Tranquil for much longer,' said the Doctor. 'Come to that, it doesn't look like a Sea! As you know, most of the Moon craters are called Sea of Something or other.'

'Yes, why's that?' asked Turlough airily.

'Galileo's doing!' said the Doctor. 'He was the first to see these vast bowls or dips on the Moon. Saw them through his telescope. He thought the dark flat areas – like the one we're sinking towards now – were seas – you know, real watery oceans' – (Turlough shook his head in disbelief at such stupidity) – 'and that the bright and rougher bits, pitted with craters, were continents of land.

'These seas, as Galileo called them,' the Doctor went on, 'had names like Sea of Cold, Lake of Dreams, Bay of Billows,

Sea of Rains, and so on. Pretty fanciful for such a bleak, hard place!'

As the TARDIS began to descend, they could also see the Earth, very distant, blue and clear with a few orange patches marking the deserts, set in a sky black as night.

'Here on the Moon,' Turlough said like a cricket commentator, 'it's a clear, bright day. Not a cloud in the sky. The pitch looks pretty dusty. Chocolate brown in colour. Could do with a good roll.' Then in his own voice he said, 'I say, Doctor, is it always fine weather here?'

'The Eagle has wings,' said the Doctor.

'So it has,' said Turlough, rather puzzled. 'So what, Doctor?'

'That was the radio message of Neil Armstrong, one of the two astronauts to land on the Moon first. He sent it to Mission Control at Houston just as the Lunar module was sinking to the Moon.'

'Oh, *Armstrong*,' said Tegan, teasing the Doctor, 'why didn't you *say*. Of course, I remember now. I thought he was rather dishy, you know.'

'Yes, not bad looking, Tegan,' remarked the Doctor. 'Quite an Apollo in his way.'

'Was that why they called the mission what they did?' Tegan giggled.

Before the Doctor could answer Turlough asked, 'Where are we now?'

'As you look at the Moon from Earth, round about its equator. And slightly to the left of a centre line drawn up and down the Moon.'

'Middle-and-off, so to speak,' Turlough nodded to himself.

Out of the window, the space trio could see the ground rushing up at them. Then they felt themselves give at the knees as the TARDIS juddered to a stop.

'Tranquillity Base here. The Eagle has landed!' announced the Doctor.

'I liked the book!' said Turlough.

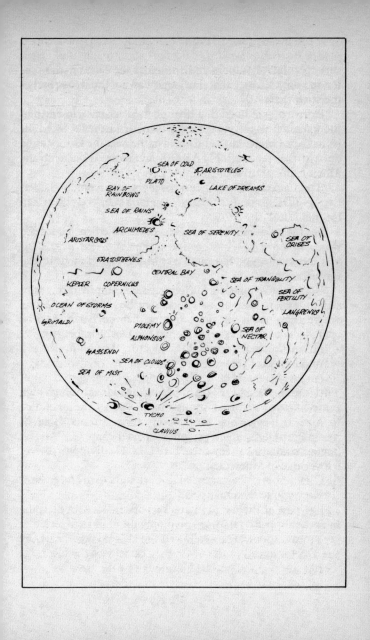

'What book?' asked Tegan.

'*The Eagle Has Landed*,' said Turlough confidently. Tegan shrugged her shoulders and smiled at the Doctor who pretended not to notice that Turlough had got the wrong end of the stick again.

'Armstrong radioed that historic message back to Earth in the evening of July twentieth, 1969. And they'd lifted off from Cape Canaveral on July sixteenth,' said the Doctor as he opened the door of the TARDIS and stepped out onto the Moon's dusty surface.

'And *that*,' bellowed Tegan over the intercom as she left the TARDIS, 'is another small step for a man – one giant leap for mankind!'

'Is that original, Tegan?' Turlough asked in his simple way.

'One small step for a man,' replied Tegan, 'is a giant leap for a Turlough!'

'Very funny!' snarled Turlough who promptly threw himself at Tegan. But he had forgotten he was on the Moon where everyone is six times lighter than on Earth. And he leaped clean over Tegan and fell at the Doctor's feet.

'Hullo, Turlough,' called the Doctor. 'Spring-heeled as a mountain goat, I see.'

'And as bright as one,' Tegan added, keeping well out of Turlough's way and the spray of fine dust his extra-high high jump had thrown up. Turlough picked up a handful of dust to hurl at Tegan but the Doctor stopped him. 'Hold it, Turlough! Don't muck the pitch up, old chap . . .' And he began striding away from the TARDIS. He disappeared over a low ridge of Moon dust.

'C'mon sport!' Tegan called to Turlough. 'Am I forgiven?'

'Race you to the lunar pod!'

The pair of them quickly picked up the knack of leaping over the slippery, dusty soil, avoiding the chunks of rock that lay strewn about. They followed the clear footprints left by the Doctor ahead of them. As they came over the low ridge Tegan stopped and grabbed Turlough by the arm.

'Get a payload of that, cobber!' She pointed down the slope that lay before them. In the distance they could see the Doctor advancing towards something spindly and silvery that glinted brilliantly in the blinding sunlight.

'It isn't the platform is it?' asked Turlough excitedly. 'Look at all that red silver paper under the legs – er, if you get what I mean?'

'Dingo dogs! You're right, Turlough!' Tegan shouted at the top of her voice. 'Last to the lunar-pod's a lunar-tic!'

The pair of them hared over the dusty plain and caught the Doctor up just as he was taking an Instant photo of the contraption. Then he stepped forward, bent down and peered at one of the lunar pod's steel legs.

'Come here!' the Doctor called out. 'See the ladder here? The one that the first real man on the moon climbed down. Now look below it!'

Turlough and Tegan bent to take a closer look. Glittering in the sun was an armband of steel clamped to the leg just below the ladder.

'Yarroo, Doctor!' cried Turlough in wonder. 'Let's get it off!'

'Allow me!' said the Doctor, deftly unclipping the armband. When it was off two curved sheets of steel opened, on hinges, like the board covers of a book, a little bigger than a paperback. On the inside of one steel sheet was engraved a pair of circles, each with a map of half the world on them. Below the circles was cut this message:

HERE MEN FROM THE PLANET EARTH
FIRST SET FOOT UPON THE MOON
JULY, 1969 A.D.

Below that were the three signatures of the astronauts: Neil Armstrong, Michael Collins, Edwin (known as Buz)

Aldrin, and a fourth signature of Richard M. Nixon, President of America at the time.

'Well, what do you know . . .?' Turlough remarked.

'Not much!' Tegan cracked, then slipped round the other side of the lunar pod before Turlough could hit her. The Doctor replaced the steel band.

The space trio spent the rest of the morning looking for footprints left by earlier astronauts.

'Know what I'd like, Doctor?' Tegan asked suddenly. The Doctor looked at her. 'Lunch?' 'Yes, that,' replied Tegan, 'and a ride in one of those Moon Buggies!' The trio slipped back to the TARDIS for a quick bite to eat first. As they sat munching their Space Snacks, Tegan asked. 'What do astronauts eat, Doctor?'

'Because of zero G,' said the Doctor, 'you know, weightlessness, they cannot cook. So they have to eat freeze-dried food pellets.'

'Oooh, like rabbits!' squawked Tegan.

'Not as bad as all that,' said the Doctor. 'I mean, they have things like shrimp cocktail, beef salad, salmon, creamed peas—'

'I rather go for mushy ones, myself,' said Turlough sipping his orange juice.

'That can be arranged, Turlough, I am sure,' said the Doctor. 'For afters their day's rations run to banana pudding and biscuits. It's quite funny eating in zero G. You can throw your food in the air and catch it as it floats about before your eyes.'

'What's it like living in weightlessness?'

'Fascinating,' said the Doctor, 'but it has its dangers, Turlough. You see, in space you're almost bedridden so the body runs down. The danger's worse in zero G, however. As your blood is weightless, the old heart doesn't have much of a load to pump round the body. So your vein walls go soft. Then when you get back to normal gravity on the Earth, say, the old ticker could give up under the sudden strain. Your heart could stop dead!'

'What do astronauts *do* then?' asked Tegan, really worried now.

'Oh, the medics have worked out ways of making the blood stream go in pulses. The astronauts wear arm bands like the doctor puts round your arm when he takes your blood pressure. This squeezes and lets go by turns to create surges in the blood flow. This keeps the heart up to the mark.' The Doctor put down his cup of Tang. 'Ready for that buggy ride?' He quickly programmed the TARDIS to take off and land about a thousand miles away in the Sea of Rains.

The Doctor led them out of the TARDIS. 'Look, chaps, the Apennine Mountains!'

Turlough looked really puzzled. 'But I thought they were in Italy . . .'

'They are, Turlough,' the Doctor beamed at his little jest, 'but *these* are the lunar Apennines. Named after the Italian ones. And here we are in Hadley Rille!'

'Rilly, Doctor?' Tegan cackled.

The trio surveyed the winding valley in which they had landed, tucked into the foot of the Apennines. Turlough kicked up a huge cloud of dust by mistake. 'Doctor, I say, the rocks here are much lighter than back in the Sea of What's-it where we've come from. Why's that?'

The Doctor picked up a handful of dust and weighed it in his hand. 'Lighter, Turlough?' he asked, puzzled. 'Ah, I get you! Lighter in *colour*! The other rocks were lava flow from a volcano. These are made of different stuff. Much, much older. They date back nearly four thousand six hundred million years. So when do you think the meteor hit the Moon to make this Sea of Rains, eh?'

Luckily Tegan came to Turlough's rescue by yelling, 'The Stars and Stripes! See, over there!' And sure enough there was the American flag, sticking out stiffly from a thin pole stuck in the Moon dust.

'Pretty windless day, you note,' said Turlough.

'There never *is* any wind on the Moon, you loon!' snorted Tegan.

Next to the flag was the familiar sight of a lunar pod, the portable launch-pad left behind by the Apollo 15 crew. And next to it, to Tegan and Turlough's delight, stood a shiny, silver lunar rover car.

'Crumbs!' exclaimed Turlough, 'Great wheels – chunky with deep, deep treads on them. It's a go-kart with no sides – Hey! What's that at the back, Doctor?'

'A parasol, can't you see?' whispered Tegan.

The Doctor put her right: 'It's a solar panel, Tegan! It charges up the electric batteries which the lunar car runs off.'

'Can we have a go?' the Terrible Two chimed.

The Doctor deftly checked the batteries and switched on the solar parasol, as Tegan called it. In no time he had it going. For the next hour Turlough and Tegan took it in turns to cruise silently round the valley. It bounced and jolted more than a dodgem at a fun fair. When they took a boulder at speed it flew on through space before bouncing onto the ground in a cloud of orangey dust. 'Better than Evel Knievel!' yelled Tegan. Then the lunar car conked out.

'Battery's run down, I expect,' remarked the Doctor. 'Anyway, you two, time we were getting back to the TARDIS. A Moon day is not that much longer than a day on Earth.'

'How long is it, then?' asked Turlough, stepping out of the lunar car.

'Only about three hours longer than the Earth's day and night,' said the Doctor picking up some of the orange dust in his gloved hand. 'See this? Guess what it's made of!'

'Gold?' suggested Tegan hopefully.

'No such luck, Tegan,' said the Doctor. 'No, it's made of tiny balls of glass. When the meteorite dented this part of the Moon it heated up the soil and fused it to glass beads. Well, chop chop, back to the TARDIS.'

As the TARDIS took off from the Moon, the Doctor gave them a guided tour of some of the craters they could see as they left them below. They even took in the other face of the Moon: it looked much the same as the face Earthlings see.

'That tiny one is called Galileo,' he said, 'but that great big crater is called Hell – after some churchman who lived about Galileo's time.

'It sure is a helluva crater, Doctor!' Tegan, as usual had had the last word.

Quiz

1. What did Neil Armstrong's radio message back to Mission Control 'The Eagle has wings' mean?

2. The Doctor said, 'One of the craters on the Moon is named after Kepler.' Who was Kepler and what was his first name?

3. Why do most maps of the Moon – not ours in this book! – always show the Moon upside down?

4. Where did the Doctor and his friends land on the Moon? Clue: The Sea of . . .

5. Tegan said, 'One small step for a man is a giant leap for a Turlough!' What did Neil Armstrong actually say when he set foot on the Moon?

Caught in a Shuttle's Scuttle

The TARDIS was Space-Time cruising back from outer space in the year AD 2111 towards Earth in AD 1983. The Doctor ran the Video Reader. 'Let's see what the papers say for Wednesday, the twenty-second of June,' he said to Tegan and Turlough. He read choice bits from the clippings from his favourite newspapers round the world to his companions.

'Tegan, what do you think of this? America's first woman into space. *Doctor* Sally Ride. Right on schedule the US space shuttle Challenger blasted off on the eighteenth of June, from the Canaveral launch pad. Oh, look, they've got ants on board.'

'Ants in your space pants!' Tegan guffawed. 'Could be nasty!'

'Apparently they're Carpenter ants,' said the Doctor drily, 'so they eat wood. They're going to see what weightlessness does to them. Ah, this is interesting: Sally is going to catch a satellite by using the Challenger's fifteen-foot folding arm.'

'What, a sort of grab, Doctor?' asked Turlough. 'Like you get in an amusement arcade?'

'I'm glad to say I've never been in one, Turlough,' said the Doctor, 'but I imagine that's the sort of thing. A long, light arm with a gentle remote-controlled pincer at the end that shoots out of the Challenger's payload bay. Sally Ride is going to use the grab four days into the space flight.'

'That's Wednesday, Doctor,' said Tegan looking at her watch.

'Like TODAY!' Turlough called out, looking at his.

Before the Doctor could say or do anything, the TARDIS gave a tremendous lurch and swung round onto its side. The Doctor and his companions found themselves rolling helplessly along one wall of the Control Room. Pencils, pocket computers and what-nots fell all around them.

'Capering kangaroos!' yelled Tegan in alarm.

'What on earth!' the Doctor said softly. 'Probably run into a radiation belt or a cosmic ray storm. Turlough, show a leg and switch on the Artificial Gravity machine, there's a good chap!'

Turlough, like the gymnast he was, vaulted round the Console and threw the Graviton switch. 'It's only a super spin-dryer, really, isn't it, Doctor?'

The Doctor winced at Turlough's off-hand way of putting it but before he could launch into a lecture on gravity, the trio found themselves with the ground under their feet again.

'Gave me quite a turn, Doctor!' Tegan said, picking up the odds and ends from the floor.

The Doctor strode to the door of the TARDIS, opened it for a second, then shut it with a bang. He looked quite shaken.

'What's up, Doctor?' asked Turlough.

'Know what I've just seen?' said the Doctor unusually ruffled for him. 'We're not in space. We're not on the Earth. And we're not on any planet.'

'Well, where *are* we?' Tegan cried breathlessly.

'In the Challenger!' said the Doctor. 'Can't think how it happened. Sally Ride must have mistaken the TARDIS for the satellite she was meant to pick up with the grab arm.'

'You sure, Doctor?' asked Turlough. 'Bit of a coincidence.'

'Like in a science fiction story,' Tegan gurgled cheerfully.

And, as in a story, there came a soft knock on the outside door.

'Doctor! Don't let them in!' hissed Turlough.

Tegan giggled. 'It's probably your Headmaster, Turlough. Come to take you back to sit your O-levels again!'

'I wouldn't put it past old Pie-jaw!' said Turlough.

Before he could enlarge on his Headmaster's quirks of behaviour, the door flew open and there stood a young, athletic brunette woman. Her face fell as she surveyed the Time trio.

'Now I've seen everything!' she trilled, calling back over

her strong shoulders to the Commander of the Challenger. 'Hey, Bob, we've found life! Life in space!'

A tall, muscular dark-haired man rushed in to join her.

Turlough croaked in fear, 'Heavens! Aliens! Tegan, don't tell them your name!'

The Doctor quickly took charge of events. Stepping forward and straightening his blazer, he extended a well-cuffed friendly hand.

'I'm the Doctor. And this is Tegan . . . and Turlough. My team! You must be Sally Ride . . . and you, Robert Crippen.'

'Nice ride?' Tegan quipped merrily.

'That's my line,' Bob smiled. 'We've heard of you, Doctor. Of *course*! Wanna come and look over the ship?'

'Yessiree!' Tegan whooped in her best American 'B' film drawl.

'Delighted,' said the Doctor quietly.

Sally stepped forward, shook their hands, then said in some surprise, 'Well, did you ever, Doctor . . . you've even got gravity laid on. 'Fraid it's all weightless back in the Challenger.'

'My gravity machine,' the Doctor muttered modestly. 'But don't worry, where we go we're used to Zero G!' Tegan was already through the door of the TARDIS and into the Challenger's payload bay. But Turlough hung back looking worried.

'What's up with him?' asked Sally briskly. 'Looks as if he's got the weight of the world on him.'

'Like Charles Atlas, you mean?' the Doctor chuckled. 'Though, I've always thought a child could hold the world up. It holds itself up in space! As for Turlough, I think he's worried lest you've got his Headmaster on board.'

'Nope,' Sally smiled, 'just us five astronauts. That's all.'

'Well, if you're sure,' said Turlough doubtfully.

'Come and see our Carpenter ants!' Sally called gaily and Turlough trotted along after her. The Doctor, last out of the TARDIS, shut the door and joined the others who had already introduced themselves all round. Sally took the

Doctor on a 'floating' tour of the Challenger. She showed him over the living quarters in the nose of the Challenger. 'When we wash, or shower,' she explained, 'air from a vacuum cleaner sucks the dirty water into a waste unit. And of course we don't need mattresses since it's weightless up here.'

Sally glided with the Doctor almost literally in tow to the space lab at the heart of the Challenger. They saw the Carpenter ants, which had quickly got used to Zero G and were busy chewing wood and making their own space colony. 'The spiders didn't catch on quite so quickly,' Sally told the Doctor.

'You remember they took Arabella and Anita, two lady spiders, in the Skylab satellite – the world's largest payload in space – way back in '73. Arabella couldn't get the hang of spinning a web at first but she quickly got used to Zero G.

Anita took to it like a duck to water, however.'

'Didn't they also take up some minnows?' the Doctor asked.

'That's right,' said Sally. 'The minnows taken up from Earth swam round drunkenly in tight loops. But their babies, hatched in space from eggs, swam quite normally.'

'And behind this lot is what?' asked the Doctor.

'More equipment,' replied Sally, 'and, of course, the rocket engines to get us back to Earth.'

'Which reminds me,' said the Doctor looking at his watch, 'time we got back to the TARDIS.'

The Doctor and his companions said goodbye to the Commander, Sally Ride, and the other three astronauts. They stepped back into the TARDIS. Sally Ride controlled the release of the TARDIS from the Challenger's pay load bay and the TARDIS floated off into space once more under the Doctor's control.

Inside the TARDIS, the Doctor and his companions chattered about their visitors from the Shuttle.

'You know, Doctor, for a moment I thought Sally was an E.T. walking in on us. What I mean is, are there any E.T.s circling the Earth in UFO's?' Turlough asked.

'Unidentified Flying Objects, eh?' sighed the Doctor. 'I tell you, I've studied the reports of the thousands of sightings. Many near airfields where they launch weather balloons and where there's no question of them being *UN*identified! All I can say is this: if there *are* intelligent aliens in those UFOs, why don't they use their intelligence? I mean, what a dim way to try to make contact with mankind. They've had plenty of time to study us!'

'Perhaps we'll get an answer to our ones and noughts message – that would be fantastic!' Tegan chattered excitedly.

The Doctor yawned. 'We'll have to wait and see. Right now, I could do with some sleep.'

And they all had a good night's rest.

Quiz

1. What was the first living creature to orbit the Earth in space?

2. What was the real advantage of using the Shuttle?

3. Who were the other space-men in the Challenger with Sally Ride?

A Ride on a Moonbeam

It was pleasantly cool outside the Cafe Bolwerk in the little
Swiss mountain town of Bern. The Doctor and his two
companions had just got there one summer evening in the
year 1905 – a red letter date in every scientist's calendar, for
reasons which will become clear. The end of the high street
was noisy with trams and people on their way home from
work. The Doctor checked the local time: seven o'clock. He
sat down at an empty table outside the coffee house and
ordered coffee and cream for three from the waiter who came
to take his order.

'Could I have a slice of apple strüdel, Doctor?' Tegan
asked, her mouth already watering at the thought of the rich
goody.

The Doctor ordered for her in German then added, 'He
should be along any minute now.'

'Not old Pie-jaw, I hope,' Turlough said with a mirthless
laugh.

'No, Turlough, not your Headmaster,' the Doctor
chuckled and poured the coffee the waiter had brought.
'And, if I'm not very much mistaken, here he is!'

Turlough's and Tegan's heads turned to see walking
towards them a short, stocky, dreamy young man with a
shock of dark hair and little moustache. In his high wing-
collar, bow-tie, and baggy ill-fitting suit he looked rather
clownish to Tegan who giggled through a mouthful of
strüdel, 'Charlie Chaplin, Doctor?'

'No, Tegan,' the Doctor whispered, 'but someone just as
famous – or rather he *will* be!' The Doctor waved and called
out, 'Albert Einstein, I believe. Would you do us the honour
of taking coffee with us?' The Doctor always talked in a
stilted way with Great Men, especially if they weren't
English.

The stocky young man stopped, bowed ever so slightly and sat down at the spare place at the Doctor's table. The Doctor introduced everyone and ordered Albert a coffee.

'I usually stop by at the Bolwerk for a chat and a drink, on my way home,' said Albert.

'What great scientific idea have you been working on today?' Tegan fired at him in her blunt Australian way. But her question boomeranged back on her.

Albert teaspooned some white sugar into his coffee thoughtfully. 'Well, today, I had to check through a long description of a new deadly weapon . . .' He watched the sugar dissolve. 'A pop-gun!' He chuckled when he saw Tegan's face fall. The Doctor, too, looked puzzled. Turlough drank his coffee blithely, and broke the silence. 'Don't tell me, sir: it didn't work.'

'Let me explain,' said Albert, with a twinkle in his eye. 'You see, Doctor, I work in the Bern Patents Office. And I have to look at a lot of plans for dud inventions. If they're not dull, they're frankly hare-brained.'

'Ever thought of doing physics?' the Doctor asked airily, 'You know about energy and mass and space and time and so forth?'

'Don't tell anyone, Doctor,' Albert said mock seriously, 'But I do . . . in my spare time. In fact, I get quite a lot of time to write about my scientific theories *in the office*! I just have to be ready to slide my papers into a drawer when I hear footsteps approaching my little cubby hole.'

'I used to do that, sir,' said Turlough chattily, 'when I was reading comics during prep.'

The Doctor shot Turlough a black look then turned to Albert and said, 'I see, and what theory are you working on at the moment?'

'As a matter of fact, four different ones!' said Albert, his merry eyes gazing toward the distant mountain peaks.

The Doctor sat up. 'Four! That's rather a lot to have on the go.'

'One of them is on the maths of how sugar dissolves in

75

coffee,' said Albert, spooning some grains of sugar from his cup. 'But that wouldn't interest you. The theory that really intrigues me is all about light and how fast it moves. I call it my Theory of Relativity.'

'I know,' Tegan piped up, 'everything is relative. That sort of thing.'

'Not quite, young lady,' Albert said gently. 'After all, you might just as well say "Everything is more!!"'

'Just so,' said Turlough easily, 'Or "Everything is less".' Albert nodded absent-mindedly, so Turlough expanded his theory. 'Or you might say, "Everything is more or less".' Tegan burst out laughing but Turlough, instead of sloshing her, looked dignified.

Albert pointed to the Moon that had just crept out from behind a snowy mountain. 'When I was in my teens I used to wonder what it would be like to ride on a moonbeam.'

Turlough looked thoughtful. 'Pretty zippy, sir?'

'Ach!' Albert smiled, 'The zippiest in the world! The fastest thing in the world . . . in space . . . in the whole universe. *That* is my First Law.'

'And your second?' prompted the Doctor, all ears. Even Tegan was silent.

'My Second Law is not *really* mine, it was Newton's,' replied Albert, now miles away in his thoughts.

'Oh we met him, didn't we?' Tegan blurted out. But fortunately Albert didn't hear her and went on dreamily, 'Newton said this: If you do an experiment on Earth or on the Moon or in a spacecraft, coasting smoothly along, you'll always get the same answer. Smooth movement won't upset your results. That's what I call my Rule of Relativity, if you get me . . .'

'More or less!' Tegan giggled, fidgeting restlessly.

Albert looked at Tegan. 'Suppose, young lady, I ask "How are we moving?"'

'Well,' Tegan drew in a deep breath then plunged in with, 'You could say we're sitting still outside the Cafe Bolwerk-and-Doctor-could-I-have-another-strüdel?'

'I'm sitting still, anyway,' said Turlough snootily.

Albert called the waiter over and ordered more coffee and strüdels. It was now dusk and all the lights in the town had come on. 'Ach so,' he went on, 'or you *could* say we're rushing through space round and round the Sun. And that old Moon up there tags along like a dog on a lead. You English have a saying "You never can tell from where you sit." Well, it's the other way round. You can only tell from where you sit. It just depends what you measure things from. To me, young lady, you are sitting still – well, *relatively* speaking!' Albert broke off to enjoy his Germanic joke. 'But to the man in the moon we are dashing around. That, my friends, is relativity.'

'So what?' Tegan said bluntly, tucking into her strüdel.

'Good question!' said Albert, not in the least put out by her brusqueness. Just then a passing tram, lit up cosily inside, rumbled by. 'Imagine, my friends, that we are riding on that tram. It is going away, as you observe, from the clock tower at the end of the *strasse*. The clock face is lit up and shows eight o'clock. Imagine the tram is moving at the speed of light. As if it were riding on a moonbeam.'

The Doctor coughed politely. 'Would it help if we actually went on a 'lightning' tram?'

The great scientist – Albert, not the Doctor – looked only mildly surprised. 'What, travel on a tram at the speed of light, Doctor? I've often dreamed of it but to do it . . . well!'

'That can be arranged,' said the Doctor mysteriously. He took out of his pocket a tiny black box. He pressed several keys on it in quick order.

'Oh *that* old thing,' snorted Tegan. 'It's the Doctor's TransMat Machine,' she explained to Albert who looked none the wiser, but full of child-like wonder.

'Trans-Materialisation, you see,' Turlough puffed himself up like a proud pigeon. 'The basic principle, as I understand it, is—'

'Cut it, sport!' Tegan interrupted Turlough's moment of glory. 'Dr Einstein probably dreams up a couple of

TransMats every day for tea – Hey! We're on that tram! That was quick, Doctor!'

And indeed they were – on the tram which only a moment ago was rumbling past their table outside the Cafe Bolwerk and was now whizzing along the street nearly at the speed of light. The Doctor waited for Albert Einstein to say something. Tegan stared out of the window at the buildings hurtling by. Turlough, who was used to this sort of thing, merely said: 'Hope you paid the bill, Doctor.'

Albert clapped his hands with joy. 'Just as I said in my paper! Doctor, see how the buildings are crowded together! And see how their tops seem to bend in towards us and tilt forwards. Note how crowded together they've become as well.'

'Yarroo!' shouted Turlough. 'The people have all got taller and thinner!'

'Boomeranging billabongs!' whooped Tegan. 'Everything's concertinaed! If this is the world of relativity, my name's Alice in Wonderland.'

'Look at the town clock!' said the Doctor. 'The hands have hardly moved.'

'*Natürlich,*' said Albert in German, 'Naturally, my friends. Since we are going nearly as fast as a moonbeam or the light from the clock, we'll see time go much slower.'

'Talking of time,' said the Doctor, 'perhaps we ought to be getting back.'

The Doctor reprogrammed his TransMat Machine and all four of them found themselves outside the Patents Office. 'Where I work,' said Albert, pulling a grim face. As they strolled back up the street, Albert stopped to buy some flowers for his wife from the flower seller. 'Did you see that tram going by at the speed of light?' he asked her.

'Only a glimpse. It went too fast. Must have been a dream. It looked so very short. And, do you know, Mein Herr, all the people in it looked thin, too.'

Albert thanked her and they walked on. 'You see, Doctor. We thought everybody and everything looked squashed up.

Just so did the people think the same about us. It's all relative to where you are – what you see. Kind of, how you say, tit-for-tat!'

'One thing I don't understand,' said the Doctor, 'You say that light is the top speed anywhere in the universe? Now if I shine my torch standing on this pavement, the light from it is going to shine up the street at 186 thousand miles a second, the speed of light. Right?' Albert nodded to both the Doctor's questions.

'BUT,' said the Doctor dramatically, 'if I was on that tram and shone my torch, are you telling me the light would still go at 186 thousand miles a second? Is that possible?'

'I am. And it is!' Albert chuckled. 'If you want to see how the maths works out, you'd better read my paper on it. It comes out next year . . . *Güten Abend*, Gentlemen, Lady! Good evening!'

The Doctor bowed with his usual old-world courtesy. And with that Albert Einstein padded off up a side street on his way home. Tegan yelled after him, '*Güten nacht*, cobber!'

'Good enough to you, Tegan!' Turlough quipped.

'Time to be getting back to the TARDIS,' said the Doctor. When they were safely inside, the Doctor began to explain what Einstein had been telling them. To Turlough's relief Tegan managed to stop him in his tracks. With a wicked gleam in her eye, she asked innocently, 'Doctor, you did pay the bill at the cafe, didn't you?'

The Doctor went quite red and stuttered, 'Up to a point . . .'

'You mean,' chuckled Tegan, 'relatively speaking!'

Quiz

1. 'Albert Einstein had written four of his brilliant scientific papers, including the one on relativity, when we met him,' says the Doctor. 'How old do you think Einstein was *then*?'

2. 'Do you think it is *really* true about clocks going slower when they travel through space very fast?' the Doctor asks.

3. 'Talking of "slow time at high speed", what do you think of this?' asks the Doctor. 'Some time in the distant future a spaceship may leave the Earth bound for a "near-by" galaxy – perhaps the Andromeda Galaxy, a mere two million light years away. The ship will travel at a speed very close to the speed of light – like the TARDIS! The trip will need only thirty years to get there and thirty years to get back to Earth. So the chaps on the ship will age only . . . how long? And how much older do you think this tired old world will be?'

Greetings! From E.T.

All morning Tegan had been eyeballing the screen of the TARDIS' mighty radar scanner *Cyclops*, which she had nicknamed 'Big Ears'. The Doctor had sent a message* into space and she was listening for a reply.

The Doctor strode into the Control Room. 'What *are* you doing, Tegan?'

'Playing with Big Ears, Doctor!'

'How many times have I told you, Tegan,' he snapped back, 'it's called *Cyclops* . . . after the one-eyed monster.' He sat down to fine-tune the 'monster'.

Tegan slipped over to Turlough on the far side of the room. He was idly flipping a golden £1 coin. 'The Doc's in a bit of a bate,' she whispered. 'And all because the Doctor loves Big Ears!'

'I used to like him,' said Turlough.

'Who?'

'Big Ears. You know, that chap in the Enid Blyton books. Waded through every blessed Blyton in the school library and *still* came bottom in English. Can't fathom it . . .'

The Doctor wheeled round excitedly. 'I'm getting a signal!'

'Oh, good,' said Turlough vaguely. 'Doctor, I've been flipping this flipping coin: heads we get a message, tails we don't. So far I've had 25 tails in a row. Not right, is it? Is it me or the coin?'

'Perhaps,' the Doctor snapped, 'the coin's not fool-proof!'

'Doctor!' Tegan yelled across to him, 'I thought it took simply yonks to get a message back from outer space. We'll all be in our bath chairs before we get a peep out of Big . . . er Cyclops. Surely!'

'Aha,' the Doctor beamed, 'thought of that. I programmed

*See 'Message-in-a-bottle' on page 49.

the TARDIS to go like a streak of lightning. Well, *nearly* at the speed of light. Now the planets with *intelligent* life on them—' he shot a look at Turlough – 'are light years away. Even so we won't have aged all that much waiting for a reply.'

'Why's that, Doctor?' Turlough's brow furrowed.

'Relativity, Turlough!' said the Doctor proudly. 'Thanks to Einstein, time goes more slowly the faster you go.'

'Like the old tram in Bern, you mean?' hooted Tegan triumphantly.

'Oh!' light dawned on Turlough's face. 'When you didn't pay the bill at the Cafe Bolwerk!'

'Yes,' said the Doctor, 'I mean . . . er . . . no! Look, I haven't time to explain now . . .'

The Doctor was saved further embarrassment by the sound of faint cracklings on the *Cyclop*'s audio system. The only other sound in the Control Room was that of Turlough's coin ringing again and again on the worktop bench. Suddenly Turlough let out a rugger scrum roar. 'Yarroo!'

'What now?' sighed the Doctor.

'It's landed on its *edge*, Doctor!' Turlough picked up the golden coin. He read the tiny letters cut into the milled edge. 'See what it says? DECUS ET TUTAMEN!'

'So?' The Doctor looked at him stonily. 'That's Latin for "Glory and Defence".'

'But don't you *see*, Doctor?' Turlough stuttered. 'It's an OMEN! It's from E.T.! Those are his initials in the middle. Bet you we get a signal now!'

Then they all heard it. Over the audio came an eerie, jerky voice, like an American DALEK. It spoke very slowly:

'Greetings, TARDIS! Can you hear me? Do you read me? My message reads:

> I like you, Doctor: Gee, you're swell!
> The reason why, I cannot tell.
> But this I know, and know full well,
> I like you, Doctor: Gee, you're swell!

This is E.T. Alien, signing off for the Traken Transmitting

Corporation, TTC, the planet Traken, the Solar System . . .
Roger-and-out!'

Then there was a click.

'The signal's gone dead,' said the Doctor expertly. He
switched off the *Cyclops*. Tegan did a war dance, chanting:
'Zipperdee-doodah, Zipperdee-ay, Alien signals came our
waaaay!'

'Told you, didn't I?' said Turlough proudly.

'You did, didn't you, old chap!' the Doctor beamed.
'Mark you, don't know what I'd have done without old
Einstein's relativity . . .'

'And the binary, Doctor!' Tegan hooted in his ear. 'So
there *is* life in outer space!'

'One thing still puzzles me, Doctor,' said Turlough,
scratching his carroty head like Stan Laurel. 'Who is Roger
Handout?'

The Doctor groaned. Then, smiling at Tegan, added,
'That's enough of outer space, for the mo'. Time for, as you'd
say, inner space!' And the pair went off into the kitchen to
rustle up some grub. Turlough stood alone flipping his golden
coin, still puzzled but all the same very chuffed with himself.

Answers

Aero-quiz

1. The *Flyer* would fit once comfortably into the Jumbo's tail.

2. 'A simple problem in ratio,' says the Doctor. 'The *Flyer* went at 30 mph and *Concorde* goes at twice the speed of sound or 15 mph. So the ratio is 2400/16 or 150. *Concorde* goes 50 times faster than the *Flyer* did.'

3. 'The Jumbo weighs 300 tons which is 300 × 2240 lbs as there are 2240 lbs in a ton. Call it 2000 lbs in round figures. So the Jumbo is 300 × 2000 lbs to the *Flyer*'s 750 lbs. That makes the Jumbo about 800 times heavier.'

The Russian Space Dreamer

'Rearrange the letters and you get TSIOLKOVSKY,' says the Doctor. 'He was Konstantin Tsiolkovsky.'

Back-garden Rocket

'Robert Goddard Hutchings,' says the Doctor. 'His name is remembered today by the Goddard Space Centre in America.'

Whiz-bangs and Rockets Quiz

1. 'Fritz Lang, the famous German film director,' chuckled the Doctor, 'would you believe! It happened like this – in Germany in the 1930s, their Society for Space Travel was asked to build a rocket to promote a film, *The Girl in the Moon*, directed by Fritz Lang. He's better known for his ghoulish mystery film '*M*', starring Peter Lorre. Well, the rocket was never made. But the film was. While it was being shot, Fritz Lang invented the count-down.'

2. 'The Chinese,' says the Doctor. 'They invented the rocket along with gunpowder way before zero A.D. – er, if you see what I mean!'

3. 'William Congreve,' says the Doctor. 'No relation, so far as I know, to the famous British playwright of that name!'

4. William Hale.

5. Peenemünde.

6. 'Wernher von Braun,' says the Doctor. (We don't like to mention what Tegan said: 'Brains as well as brawn!')

The Planets Quiz

1. 'From the story you can tell it was ten thousand million years ago,' says the Doctor. 'Scientists are cautious creatures, however, and put it between nine and sixteen thousand million years ago.'

2. 'On my London model,' the Doctor says proudly, 'the distances came out in kilometres like this: Mercury 0.4,

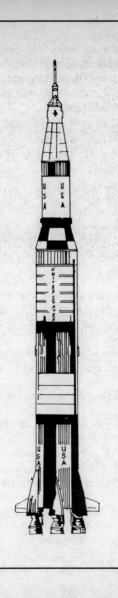

Venus 0.7, Earth 1, Mars 1½, Jupiter 5, Saturn 10, Uranus 20, Neptune 30, Pluto 40.

'To get their distances from the Sun in miles, simply multiply by 100 thousand, giving: Mercury 40,000, Venus 70,000, Earth 100,000, Mars 150,000, Jupiter 500,000, Saturn one million, Uranus two million, Neptune three million, Pluto four million miles.

'All round figures, of course. But near enough to get the sort of sizes. Actually, the Earth is not 100,000 miles from the Sun but a shade less – 93,000 miles. So my rough'n'ready figures are close enough!'

3. 'The beach ball, for Jupiter, is a metre in diameter,' says the Doctor, 'and a grapefruit is, let's say, ten centimetres across – just to keep the numbers simple. That makes Jupiter a hundred times bigger in diameter than the Earth, or 80,000 miles across. Not bad shooting, seeing the accurate figure is 88,700 miles!'

4. 'The name Turlough was searching for,' says the Doctor, 'was Copernicus. You say it "kop-*ERN*-ik-uss". He was a Polish astronomer – Nicholas Copernicus.'

5. 'Sixteen miles a second,' says the Doctor, 'or 58 thousand miles an hour. The accurate figure is 54 thousand mph.'

6. The nearest and fastest are one and the same: Mercury.

7. 'The hottest planet, as you might expect,' says the Doctor, 'is nearest the Sun: it is Mercury. It whacks up to over 300°C or 600°F, the heat of a roasting oven – so far as we can discover. The coldest planet, by the way, is the farthest out, Pluto, at an all-time low of over 200°C below zero.'

8. 'The four biggies,' says the Doctor, 'are, in order of size getting smaller: Jupiter, Saturn, Uranus, and Neptune. The other four are much, much smaller.'

9. 'The biggest one of them all,' says the Doctor, 'Jupiter.'

10. 'Meteors are shooting stars,' says the Doctor. 'They are chunks of rock and dust. Large ones we call meteorites, which occasionally hit the Earth and leave a vast dent in it.'

11. 'Halley's Comet,' says the Doctor, 'comes round, as I told you every 76 years. The last time it was seen was in 1910. So it is due back in 1986.'

Message-in-a-Bottle Puzzle

The Doctor has kindly drawn out the rows of binary numbers for you and blacked in the zeroes. He asks: 'Can you see a little man or woman?' Turlough says, 'It's E.T.!' But Tegan thinks it looks like Turlough!

381	I●IIIII●I	
427	II●I●I●II	
455	III●●●III	*A person*
455	III●●●III	(or is it E.T.?)
439	II●II●II	
439	II●II●II	
439	II●II●II	

Puzzle Messages

A	I●●IIIII	
	II●I●I●II	*A 2-humped camel,*
	II●●●●●I	or bactrian
	III●●●●●	
	III●II●I	
	III●II●I	

91

B

I●●II●II
II●I●●●I
III●●●●I
III●II●I
III●II●I

A single-humped camel,
or dromedary

C

I●●I●●I●●I
I●●●●●●●I
I●●●●●●●I
I●●●●I●●I
I●●●II II●I
I●●●II I●●I

A castle

D

II●IIIIII
I●●●II II●
III●●●●●I
III●●●●●I
III●II I●I

A dog

Starry Puzzlers

1. 'My song,' says the Doctor, 'is an old memory jogger still used by students of astronomy. The letters *O, B, A, F, G, K* and *M* aren't notes on a musical scale! They stand for the pattern of stars in order of brightness and colour. It's to do with what we scientists call *spectral lines* seen in the light from stars. Er . . . I'd better explain that a spectre is a ghost, as you know, but these lines aren't ghosts!' (In case you're puzzled, you should know this is just one of the Doctor's little jokes!)

'We scientists analyse the light from stars in special instruments and that's how we see these spectral lines.'

'Yes, but what do the letters *stand for*?' Tegan asks impatiently.

'Coming to that,' says the Doctor. 'The *O*-stars are the heavy-weight, brilliant stars giving out mainly blue light. They are terrifically hot – anything from 50,000°C down to

25,000°C on their surface. In the middle of the *spectrum*, as we say, are the middle-weight, yellow *G*-stars – like our Sun – with temperatures of about 5,000°C. At the other end of this spectrum are the dim *M*-stars – cool, and red and ranging from 3,500°C to 1,500°C.'

'What a super explanation!' says Tegan. 'Didn't understand a word of it.' All the same she gave him a kiss, well a peck, on the cheek for his pains!

2. 'You probably know them as the signs of the zodiac,' says the Doctor. 'They were the symbols astronomers once used for the planets: Mercury, Venus, Earth, Mars, Jupiter, Saturn, Uranus, Neptune and Pluto – in that order.'

Girl on the Moon

1. Neil's message meant that he and his two co-space-men in the Apollo 11 spacecraft were in orbit round the Moon.

2. Johannes Kepler was a German astronomer who lived from 1571 to 1630.

3. Because the maps show the moon as seen through a telescope – upside-down!

4. The Sea of Tranquillity.

5. Neil said, 'One small step for a man is one giant leap for mankind.' He had probably rehearsed it!

Caught in a Shuttle's Scuttle

1. The female dog Leika in the Russian spacecraft Sputnik 2 in 1957. She never came back – as planned – and was put to sleep in flight painlessly.

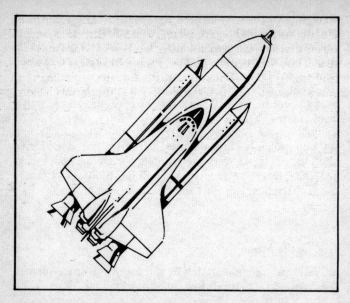

2. The Shuttle re-uses the main body of the Challenger plane which cuts down the cost of launching things into space and returning to Earth. Once-off rockets are enormously costly.

3. The others aboard the Challenger were: Rick Hauck, 42, the pilot, John Fabian, 44, who launched the satellite Sally Ride recovered – not the TARDIS! – and Dr Norman Thagood, 39, an expert in space sickness caused by Zero G conditions.

A Ride on a Moonbeam

1. Einstein was only 26 years old, staggeringly young to have completed such world-shattering ideas (literally – if you think of the Atom Bomb that came out of his idea that mass can be changed into energy in his famous equation $E = mc^2$).

2. Yes, they have sent quartz clocks in airplanes whizzing round the Equator and when the planes landed the clocks were running slow compared to quartz clocks on Earth! A fanciful but true thought: a bug sitting on the rim of an LP turning on a record player will age more slowly – not much! – than a bug sitting in the middle. People should age by a tiny, tiny fraction of a second less at the Equator (spinning at a speed) than an Eskimo at the North Pole, turning much more slowly!

3. The world would have aged, by Einstein's theory of relativity, four million years!